TRINITY GUILDHALL

Sound at Sight

Flute

Book 1

Grades 1-4

by James Rae

Published by:
Trinity College London
89 Albert Embankment
London SE1 7TP UK

T +44 (0)20 7820 6100
F +44 (0)20 7820 6161
E music@trinityguildhall.co.uk
www.trinityguildhall.co.uk

Printed in England by Halstan & Co. Ltd, Amersham, Bucks.

Sound at Sight

Sight reading requires you to be able to read and understand music notation, then convert sight into sound and perform a piece. This involves imagining the sound of the music before playing it, which in turn requires familiarity with intervals, chord shapes, rhythmic patterns and textures. The material in this series offers a wide range of examples designed to help players develop their skills and build confidence.

Examination sight reading

In an exam, you have half a minute to prepare your performance. Use this time wisely:

- Check the key and time signatures. You might want to remind yourself of the scale and arpeggio, checking for signs of major or minor first.
- Look for any accidentals, particularly when they apply to more than one note in the bar.
- Set the pace in your head and read through the piece, imagining the sound. It might help to sing part of the music or to clap or tap the rhythm. You can also try out any part of the test if you want to.
- Have you imagined the effect of the dynamics?

When the examiner asks you to play the piece, do not forget the pace you have set. Fluency is more important than anything else: make sure that you keep going whatever happens. If you make a little slip, do not go back and change it. Give a performance of the piece: if you can play the pieces in this book you will be well-prepared, so enjoy the opportunity to play another piece that you didn't know beforehand.

Candidates should always refer to the requirements listed in the most recent syllabus when preparing for an examination.

• Grade 1

Count one-beat, two-beat and four-beat notes carefully. ***mf*** (*mezzo forte*) means moderately loud.

6
Moderato
p
mf
7
Moderato
mf
p
mf
8
Moderato
mf
p
mf
9
Moderato
mf
p
f
10
Moderato
f
p
f

11
Moderato
p
mf
p
12
Moderato
f
13
Moderato
mf
f
14
Moderato
mf
15
Moderato
f
p
f

The following examples are also suitable for candidates following the jazz syllabus.

• Grade 2

The $\frac{3}{4}$ time signature is introduced, along with simple ties and slurs.

7
Moderato
mf
p
mf
8
Allegretto
mf
p
mf
9
Moderato
mf
p
mf
10
Moderato
p
mf
11
Moderato
mf
p
mf

The following examples are also suitable for candidates following the jazz syllabus.

17

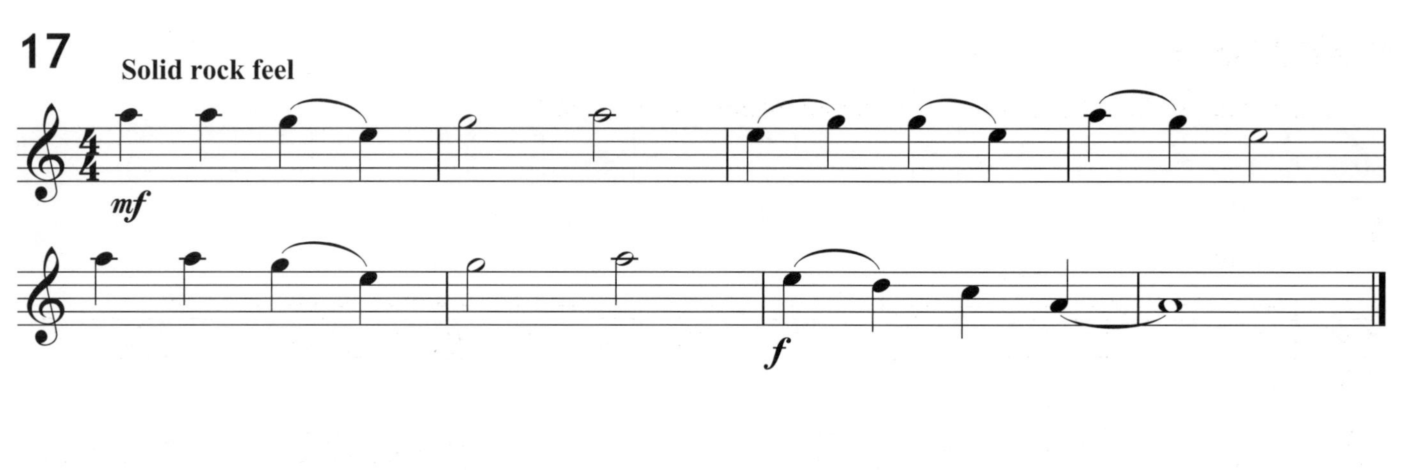

18

19

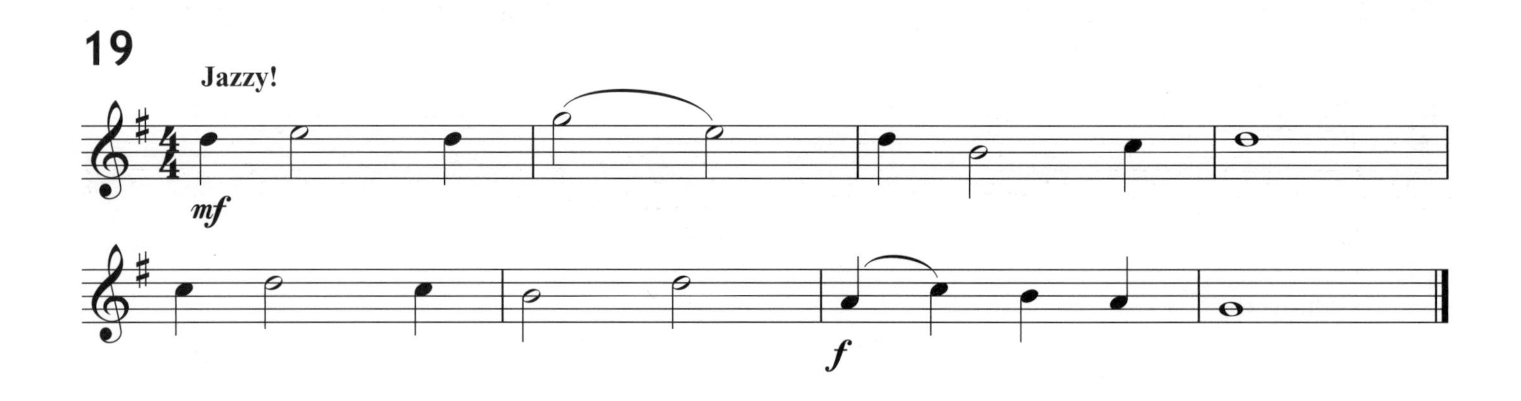

20

• Grade 3

Quavers are included at this grade. Andante means 'walking pace'.

5

Allegretto
mp
p
mf

6

Andante
mp
mf
p

7

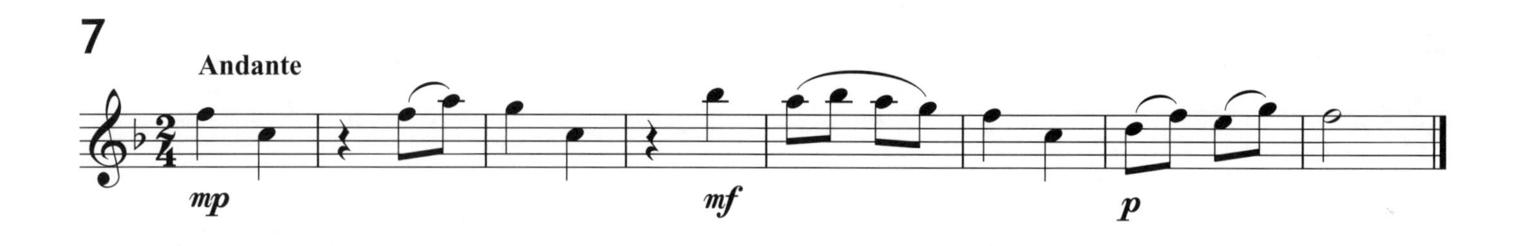
Andante
mp
mf
p

8

Allegretto
mf
mp
mf
p

9

Allegretto
mf
mp
mf

10

Andante
mf
mp
mf

11
Andante
mf
mp
mf
12
Allegretto
f
p
mp
f
p
f
13
Moderato
mf
p
mf
14
Allegretto
mf
mp
f
15
Allegretto
mf
mp
f

The following examples are also suitable for candidates following the jazz syllabus.

• Grade 4

Staccato notes are added at this grade, in addition to *crescendo* (*cresc.*) and *diminuendo* (*dim.*).

5

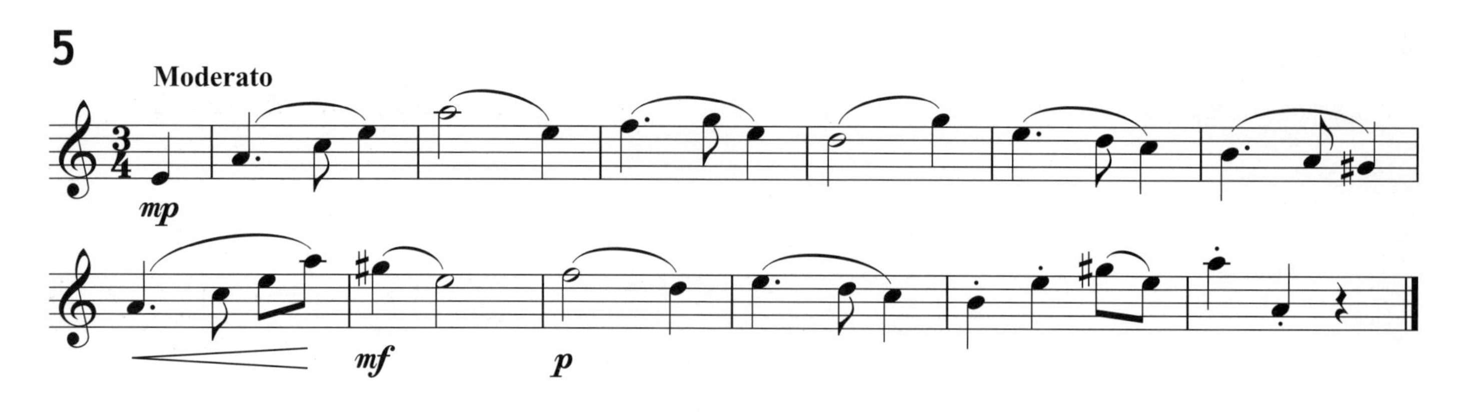
Moderato
mp
mf
p

6

Allegretto
mp
cresc.
mf
mp
p
cresc.
mf

7

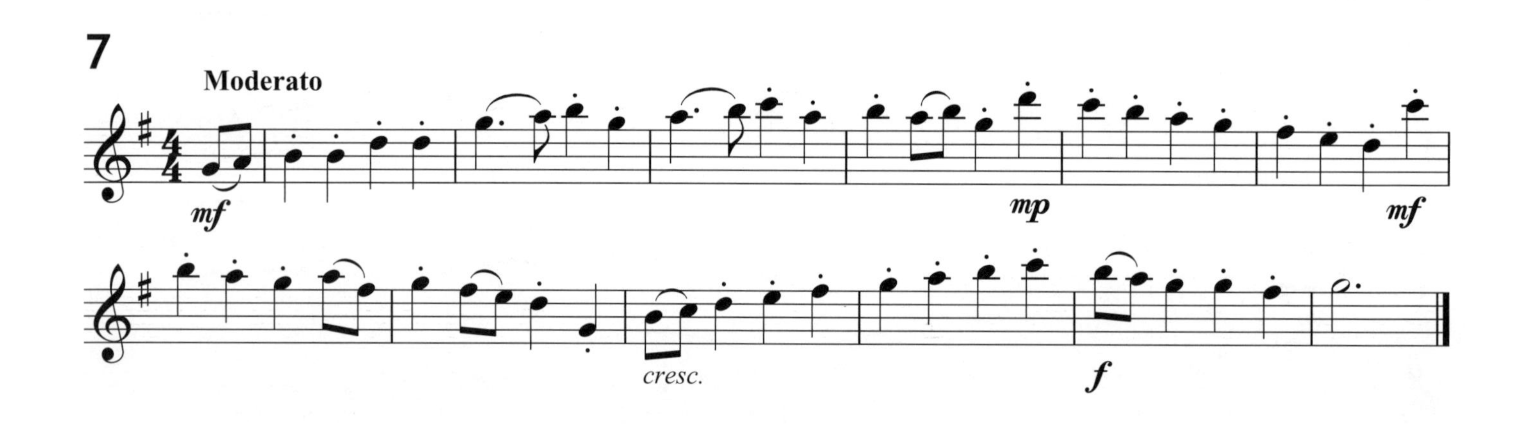
Moderato
mf
mp
mf
cresc.
f

8

Allegretto
mf
mp
mf

9
Allegretto
mf
mp
f

10
Andante
mf
mp
mf

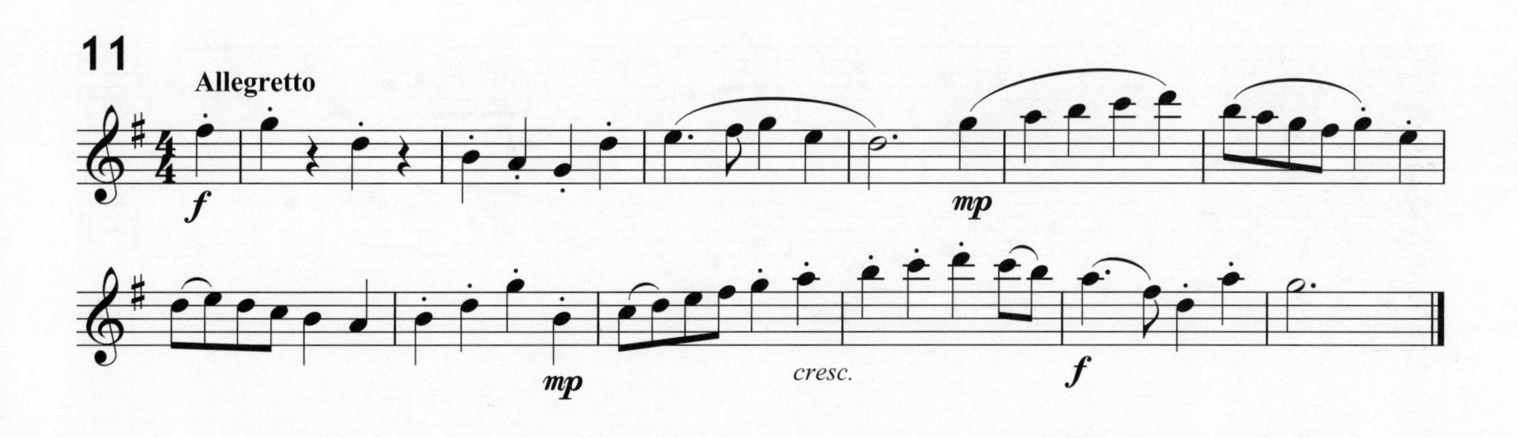
11
Allegretto
f
mp
mp
cresc.
f

12
Andante
mf
mp
cresc.
mf
dim.
p

The following examples are also suitable for candidates following the jazz syllabus.

17
Heavy rock tempo
f
18
Jazz waltz
mp
mf
mp
p
19
Swinging blues feel
mf
f
mf
f
p
f
20
Jazz waltz
mp
mf